SCHOLASTIC

English Practice for

Year 4

Ages 8–9

This book belongs to:

....

English Year 4, Book 2

Scholastic Education, an imprint of Scholastic Ltd
Book End, Range Road, Witney, Oxfordshire, OX29 0YD
Registered office: Westfield Road, Southam, Warwickshire CV47 0RA
www.scholastic.co.uk

© 2016, Scholastic Ltd

1 2 3 4 5 6 7 8 9 6 7 8 9 0 1 2 3 4 5

British Library Cataloguing-in-Publication Data
A catalogue record for this book is available from the British Library.

ISBN 978-1407-14200-5
Printed in Italy by STIGE - Turin

Editorial
Rachel Morgan, Melissa Somers, Sarah Sodhi, Catherine Baker
and Fiona Tomlinson

Design
Scholastic Design Team: Neil Salt, Nicolle Thomas
and Oxford Designers & Illustrators Ltd

Cover Design
Neil Salt

Illustration
Aleksander Sotirovski (Beehive Illustration)

Every effort has been made to trace copyright holders for the works reproduced
in this book, and the publishers apologise for any inadvertent omissions.

Contents

Why buy this book?

This series has been designed to support the introduction of the new National Curriculum in schools in England. The new curriculum is more challenging in English and includes the requirement for children's understanding to be secure before moving on. These practice books will help your child practise all of the skills they will learn at school, including some topics they might not have encountered previously.

How to use this book

- The content is divided into National Curriculum topics (for example, Spelling, Grammar, Comprehension and so on). Find out what your child is doing in school and dip into the relevant practice activities as required.

- Let your child know you are sharing the activities and support if necessary using the helpful quick tips at the top of most pages.

- Keep the working time short and come back to an activity if your child finds it too difficult. Ask your child to note any areas of difficulty. Don't worry if your child does not 'get' a concept first time, as children learn at different rates and content is likely to be covered throughout the school year.

- Check your child's answers using the answers section at the end of this book.

- Give lots of encouragement and tick off the progress chart as your child completes each chapter.

How to use the book

This tells you which topic you're working on.

This is the title of the activity.

Letters in slashes (like this) tell you it's the sound and not the spelling.

These boxes will help you with the activity.

This is the instruction text. It tells you what to do.

Follow the instruction to complete the activity.

You might have to write on lines, in boxes, draw or circle things.

The 'ch' machine

Remember, **'ch'** can be said in three different ways: **/ch/, /sh/, /k/**.

1. Complete the sentences below by writing the correct **'ch'** word.

2. Then write **'ch'**, **'sh'** or **'k'** to show how the word you have written is pronounced.

> stomach chalet scheme orchestra parachute
> architect moustache chandelier

The _____ dangled from the ceiling. ☐

I have a _____ ache. ☐

There is a wooden _____ on the hill. ☐

I have a _____ to not do my homework. ☐

The man played the violin in the _____ . ☐

The _____ drew pictures of the house. ☐

The man had a neat _____ . ☐

I jumped from the aeroplane with a _____ . ☐

Searching for 'que' and 'gue'

1. Find the words below in the wordsearch.

grotesque   opaque   fatigue

physique   unique   intrigue

antique   colleague

p	h	y	s	i	q	u	e	q
i	q	u	e	s	c	i	f	u
n	u	n	i	q	u	e	a	e
t	g	r	u	f	n	b	t	g
r	u	d	a	s	u	g	i	u
i	e	c	n	s	e	u	g	e
g	r	o	t	e	s	q	u	e
u	c	i	i	a	s	c	e	t
e	n	o	q	g	u	e	l	i
q	u	e	u	f	q	u	e	l
g	h	b	e	a	d	d	t	h
o	p	a	q	u	e	b	h	d
c	o	l	l	e	a	g	u	e

Singular to plural

There are lots of rules about how to show that nouns are plural.

- For most nouns, add **'s'**.
- Nouns ending in **'s'**, **'ss'**, **'sh'**, **'ch'**, **'x'** and **'z'**, add **'es'**.
- Nouns ending in **'y'**, take off the **'y'** and add **'ies'**.
- Nouns ending in **'f'**, take off the **'f'** and add **'ves'**.

1. Change these sentences from *singular* to *plural* by changing nouns, verbs, pronouns and other words where necessary. An example has been done for you.

The boy walks his dog.

The boys walk their dogs.

The ship hit the iceberg.

Her tooth hurts badly.

The horse is eating a raw carrot.

The cat chased the mouse through the house.

She heard the echo in the cave.

Apostrophes

Apostrophes can be used to show that something belongs to someone or something.

- *The dog's basket* – the basket belongs to the dog

1. Read the sentences below. Circle the words that are missing the possessive apostrophe and write them correctly.

  a. The strong wind blew Olivias umbrella away.

  b. The rain battered the horses stable.

  c. I saw the rabbits tail.

  d. The man fixed the boats rudder.

  e. The dogs ball rolled under the fence.

  f. I looked at my friends picture.

  g. The cars brakes squealed when it stopped.

  h. I like my brothers new bike.

If you need help, ask an adult!

Adding 'ing'

Remember, for some words you double the last consonant when you add a suffix:

- *hop – ho**pp**ing*
- *control – contro**ll**ing*

But if the first syllable is stressed you don't:

- *visit – visi**t**ing*

1. **Underline the syllable which is stressed in these two-syllable words.**

forget	limit
begin	target
travel	regret
visit	prefer
permit	fuel
admit	focus

2. **Now write the words from question 1 with an 'ing' ending.**

forget	_____	limit	_____
begin	_____	target	_____
travel	_____	regret	_____
visit	_____	prefer	_____
permit	_____	fuel	_____
admit	_____	focus	_____

/i/ word search

1. Find the words for the word search from the meanings below.

A shape with four triangle sides
and one square bottom:

_____

A story that isn't true:

_____

A dinosaur that flies:

_____

Something that we breathe:

_____

The words of a song written
down:

_____

A young swan:

_____

A clear transparent rock:

_____

Something strange or not known:

_____

m	y	s	t	e	r	y	h
u	c	o	h	y	o	r	d
p	y	r	a	m	i	d	u
t	g	a	l	y	l	a	k
e	n	u	y	t	o	w	l
r	e	o	f	h	c	r	m
o	t	x	o	y	r	e	n
d	u	y	i	r	y	y	o
a	i	g	n	e	s	n	p
c	g	e	d	w	t	h	y
t	h	n	f	b	a	x	s
y	r	e	x	n	l	o	i
l	y	r	i	c	s	i	n

What's the meaning?

1. **Draw lines to match the 'ou' word with its meaning.**

country	Having lived for a short time.
encourage	To grow successfully.
hound	A light dessert made from egg and sugar.
mousse	Baked to make bread.
nourish	To try to make someone or something do something.
flourish	Two things together.
dough	Another word for a dog.
couple	To give food for things to grow healthily.
young	A place where people live.

2. **Find three 'ou' words above which do not sound /u/ and write them below. Can you think of other words where 'ou' sounds the same?**

_____   _____

_____   _____

_____   _____

3. **Choose two of the words in question 1. Use them in a sentence of your own.**

_____

_____

Prefix crossword

1. The words in the box below begin with the prefixes **'dis'**, **'mis'**, **'in'**, **'ir'**, **'il'**, **'im'**. Match them to the clues to find the answers to the crossword.

> disappeared   illogical   misplaced   invisible
> irresistible   impossible   irregular

Across	Down
2. That cake looks too delicious.	1. Uneven.
4. Something that cannot be done.	3. It cannot be seen.
6. That doesn't make sense!	5. It was there a minute ago, but now it is not!
7. It has been put somewhere else.	

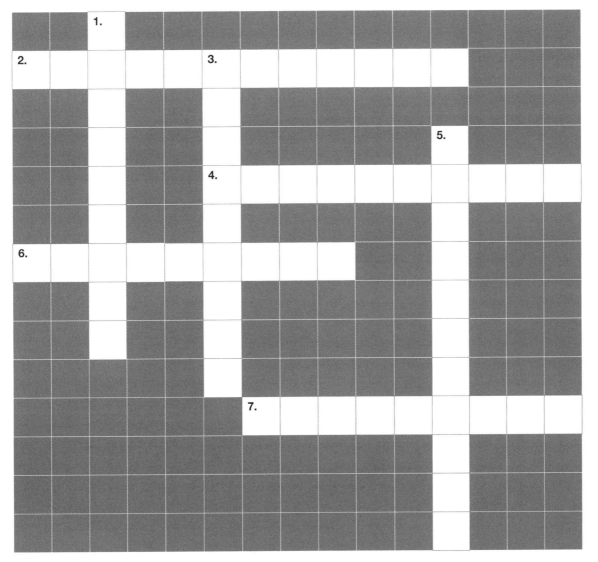

Add the correct word

1. Add the correct **'re'** or **'inter'** word to complete these sentences.

> recover   redecorate   rearrange   retreat   international
>
> interface   interval   intergalactic

a. I need to _____ after running the race.

b. The _____ on the computer looks odd.

c. The _____ is usually in the middle of the

performance.

d. The librarian will need to _____ the books.

e. The _____ space cruiser docked safely at

Saturn Beta.

f. The painter must _____ the room.

g. Global Baggage is an _____ chain of hotels.

h. When I don't want to do my homework, I _____

to my room.

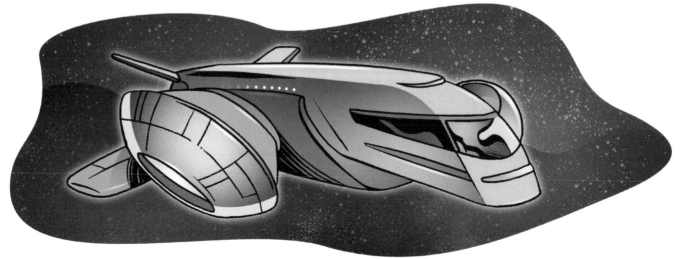

'anti' and 'auto'

- **'anti'** means *against*.
- **'auto'** means *self*.

1. Use the prefix machine to add **'anti'** or **'auto'** to these words and
   write them in the space provided.

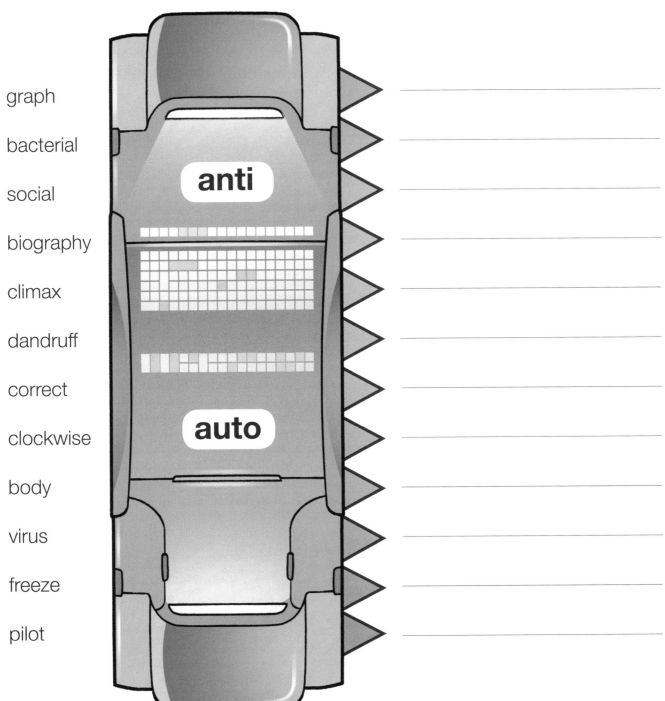

graph

bacterial

social

biography

climax

dandruff

correct

clockwise

body

virus

freeze

pilot

The missing 'ation'

1. Look at these words. Look them up in a dictionary if you need to.

> admiration   relocation   justification   translation   animation   education
> observation   accommodation   anticipation   identification

2. Use the words from question 1 to complete these sentences.

a. I was full of _____ when my friend won the cup.

b. I could not do the _____ from French to English.

c. The hotel did not have any _____ available.

d. The _____ costs were going to be huge,

so my dad didn't move.

e. The _____ was about a dog and was very funny.

f. The _____ of seeing my best friend after

the holidays was too much.

g. I want to get an _____ so I can get myself a job.

h. The _____ tag was

still on the dog so we found a phone number.

i. I didn't agree with the _____

for not letting us outside at playtime.

j. The teacher assessed the children by _____.

Quickly

An **adverb** describes a verb. Some adverbs are made by adding **'ly'** to adjectives. In the sentence *She ran quickly*, the adverb *quickly* tells us how she ran.

1. Add a different adverb to each of the following sentences.

a. Mr James ran _____ .

b. He drove _____ .

c. It rained _____ .

d. The car stopped _____ .

e. She laughed _____ .

f. Jim answered _____ .

g. The music played _____ .

h. The girl sighed _____ .

i. Jake did his homework _____ .

j. Time passed _____ .

2. Underline the adverbs in *Escape*.

Escape

He ran quickly down the street. He looked anxiously left and right. Fortunately everything was quiet. He felt tired and rather unhappy to be running away so soon. He reached the crossroads and stopped momentarily. He started again and turned cautiously into the High Street. Suddenly he stopped. There was the sound of footsteps behind him. His heart beat violently. He was being followed!

Adding 'ly' to words ending in 'ic'

If the adjective ends in **'ic'**, add **'al'** before **'ly'**: *basic – basically.*

1. Change these adjectives into adverbs by sending them round the prefix roundabouts.

dramatic

frantic

historic

domestic

energetic

diplomatic

robotic

tragic

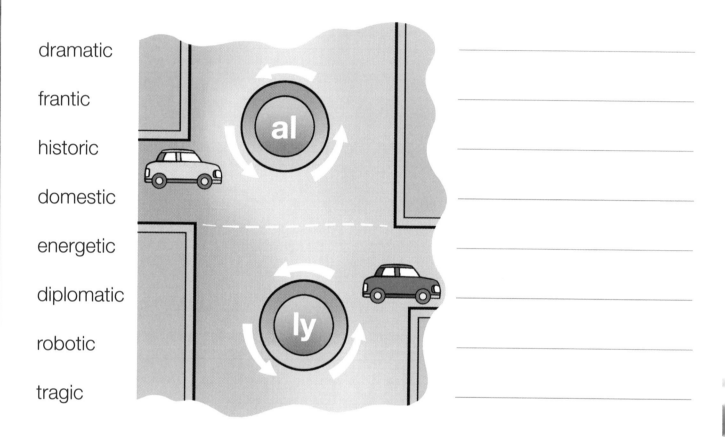

2. Choose four adverbs from question 1. Use them in sentences of your own.

A diversion

When a word ends with the sound **/zh/u/n/**, it is always spelled **'sion'**: *erosion*.

Remember to take off the **'d'**, **'de'** or **'se'** before adding **'sion'**: *erode – erosion*.

1. **Change these words by adding 'sion' and then complete the sentences.**

> comprehend   corrode   revise   divert
> confuse   allude   collide   divide

a. The maths problem required long _____ as part of

   the calculation.

b. The cars were involved in a _____ .

c. We had to take the left road because there was a _____ .

d. The wrong directions caused _____ .

e. The hole in the pipe was caused by _____ .

f. I managed to do my _____ homework.

g. My brother is trying to do his _____ for his exams.

h. I made an _____ to going to the party.

What do you do?

1. Look at these pictures of people doing their jobs. Write the appropriate 'cian' word underneath.

politics	diet	beauty

music	optics	physics
	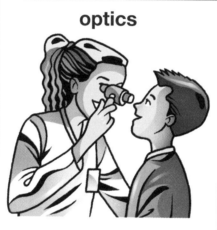	

electricity	magic	mathematics

Search for 'tion', 'sion', 'ssion'

1. **Add the correct ending to the words below and write them in the space provided. Then find them in the word search.**

confess _____   conclude _____

discuss _____   confuse _____

admit _____   complete _____

transmit _____   obstruct _____

adopt _____   explode _____

s	c	o	n	f	e	s	s	i	o	n	h	t
d	o	d	c	b	u	i	o	s	s	e	l	o
i	n	n	a	d	o	p	t	i	o	n	o	t
s	f	s	e	a	u	g	h	s	b	a	k	r
c	u	x	c	a	n	d	u	r	s	d	o	a
u	s	y	c	o	m	p	l	e	t	i	o	n
s	i	s	t	s	t	e	s	s	r	s	s	s
s	o	m	r	e	d	e	d	e	u	s	s	m
i	n	a	a	m	r	t	y	u	c	i	p	i
o	e	t	e	a	b	r	o	u	t	v	e	s
n	s	s	a	d	m	i	s	s	i	o	n	s
o	s	e	x	p	l	o	s	i	o	n	r	i
c	o	n	c	l	u	s	i	o	n	c	f	o
i	b	d	s	s	i	o	n	s	u	k	c	n

The 'ch' machine

Remember, **'ch'** can be said in three different ways: **/ch/**, **/sh/**, **/k/**.

1. **Complete the sentences below by writing the correct 'ch' word.**

2. **Then write 'ch', 'sh' or 'k' to show how the word you have written is pronounced.**

> stomach   chalet   scheme   orchestra   parachute
> architect   moustache   chandelier

The _____ dangled from the ceiling. ☐

I have a _____ ache. ☐

There is a wooden _____ on the hill. ☐

I have a _____ to not do my homework. ☐

The man played the violin in the _____. ☐

The _____ drew pictures of the house. ☐

The man had a neat _____. ☐

I jumped from the aeroplane with a _____. ☐

Searching for 'que' and 'gue'

1. Find the words below in the word search.

grotesque   opaque   fatigue

physique   unique   intrigue

antique   colleague

p	h	y	s	i	q	u	e	q
i	q	u	e	s	c	i	f	u
n	u	n	i	q	u	e	a	e
t	g	r	u	f	n	b	t	g
r	u	d	a	s	u	g	i	u
i	e	c	n	s	e	u	g	e
g	r	o	t	e	s	q	u	e
u	c	i	i	a	s	c	e	t
e	n	o	q	g	u	e	l	i
q	u	e	u	f	q	u	e	l
g	h	b	e	a	d	d	t	h
o	p	a	q	u	e	b	h	d
c	o	l	l	e	a	g	u	e

S(c)ounds like

1. **All of these words use 'sc' in their spelling but they don't all sound the same. Sort the words according to their sound.**

> scented   descent   discipline   adolescent   escape
> scream   scooter   oscillate   ascent   score   disco   scarf

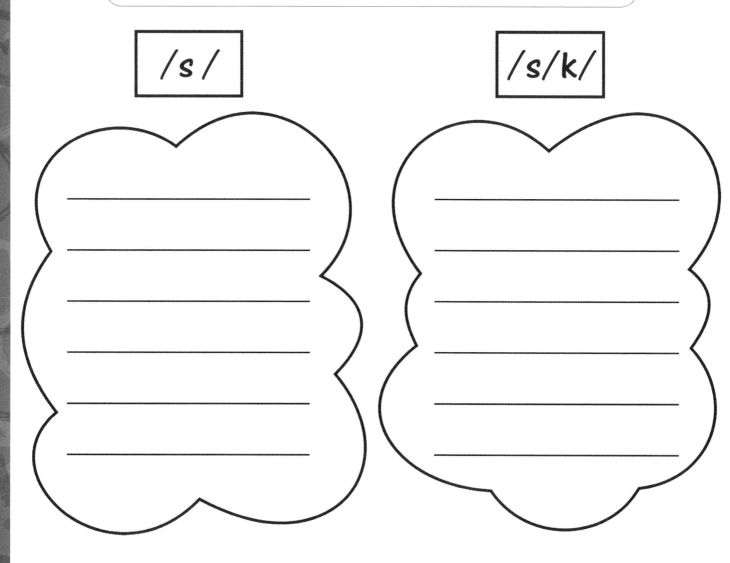

/s/

/s/k/

2. **Look at the two groups of words.**

What letters follow **'sc'** in words that sound like **/s/**?

_____

What letters follow **'sc'** in words that sound like **/s/k/**?

_____

/ai/ sound

a astray away bay betray
castaway clay convey day
decay delay dismay disobey
display eight essay fray grey
holiday hooray jay lay may

mislay nay neigh neighbour
obey pay play portray pray
prey ray repay say sleigh
spray stay stray subway sway
they vein weigh yesterday

1. **Look at this extract from a rhyming dictionary with words that have the long /ai/ vowel sound. Find suitable words to complete the second and last verses of this ballad.**

Silly Billy

Now, here's the tale of Billy boy,

A tale we should all convey.

For Billy acted without thought,

He's a silly boy today.

Now Billy was a silly boy,

He just wanted to _____

So instead of going to school one day

He ran away in a _____

Now Billy was a silly boy,

He didn't want to _____

And now instead of being at school,

He's led himself _____

A be poem

1. Read this poem below and then rewrite it using the correct homophones.

There was a little be

Who flew across the see

Because he said he new

That the sea was a lovely bright blew

_____

_____

_____

_____

Homophone sentences

1. **Add the correct homophone to complete the sentences.**

I had to _____ a letter to my grandparents to thank them for

my present. **right** / **write**

You have to wait _____ until the lights turn green. **here** / **hear**

The match was called off because of the _____.

whether / **weather**

You should have _____ the queue for the sale! **seen** / **scene**

2. **Write some sentences to show the meanings of these homophones.**

knot / not _____

_____

_____

heel / heal / he'll _____

_____

_____

_____

medal / meddle _____

_____

_____

Homophone word search

1. Write the homophones of these words.

   fare _____

   mist _____

   peace _____

   grown _____

2. Now find all eight words in the word search.

f	a	r	e	s	s	g	h
a	c	m	r	e	f	h	m
p	o	i	f	a	i	r	i
i	g	s	h	o	d	i	s
e	r	t	i	p	l	a	s
c	o	e	p	e	a	c	e
e	w	s	a	d	r	m	d
x	n	s	g	r	o	a	n

Boy overboard

In English, many words which sound the same are spelled differently to show different meanings. Words of this kind are called **homophones**. It is interesting to note dialect differences: *ant* and *aunt* are pronounced in the same way by Northerners but not by Southeners, and *bomb* and *balm* are pronounced the same way by Americans!

1. **Read each sentence, then respell the words in italics so that they give the correct meaning.**

   a. Throw that *boy* _____ overboard!

   b. I enjoy watching *cereals* _____ on television.

   c. There was a long *cue* _____ for snooker yesterday.

   d. I would like a good quality bow made out of *you* _____.

   e. I am sorry to tell you that she *dyed* _____ yesterday.

   f. The baker had to *need* _____ the dough.

   g. Oh, I see that you've had your *hare* _____ done!

   h. This fake *fir* _____ coat is very prickly.

   i. I can't help until I get the *fax* _____.

   j. London has elected a new *mare* _____.

2. **Make up more humorous sentences of the same kind.**

   _____

   _____

Creating nouns

1. Join the words to the prefixes and then write the noun that is created.

	Prefix	Noun
violet		_____
cover		_____
sound		_____
port		_____
arm		_____
marine		_____
atlantic		_____
ground		_____
late		_____

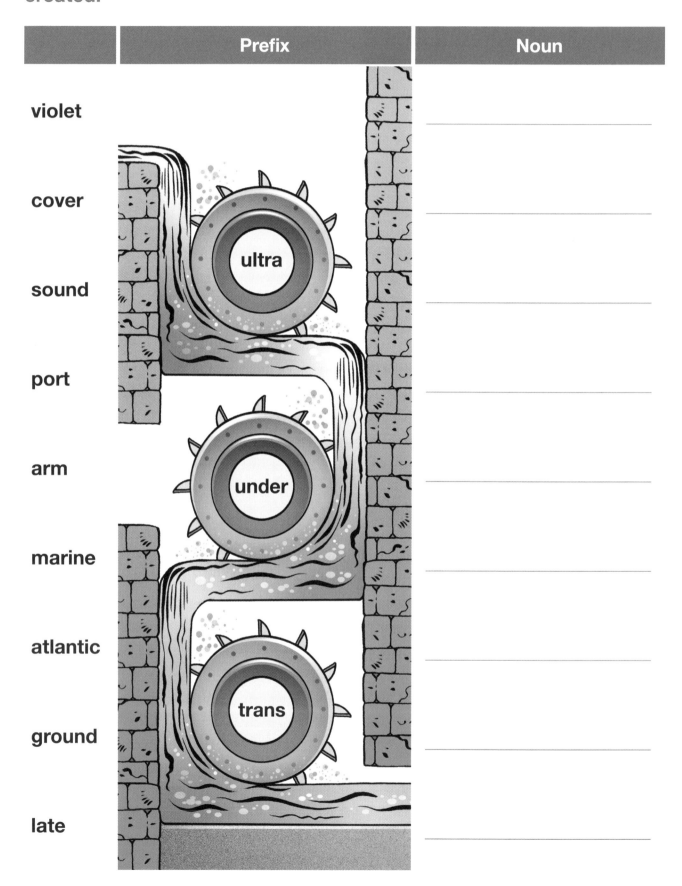

ultra

under

trans

From *porto* to *porter*

1. Here are some more words with roots from older languages.
   Complete the table by finding more modern words for each word
   family.

Root word	Modern word	More words
porto (carry)	porter	
rota (wheel)	rotate	
scribe (write)	describe	
unus (one)	unit	
vanus (empty)	vanish	
video (see)	video recorder	

Word families (1)

A **word family** is a group of words formed from the same root by adding different **prefixes** and **suffixes**. An example is given below for *electric*.

1. Make a word family for the word *profess*.

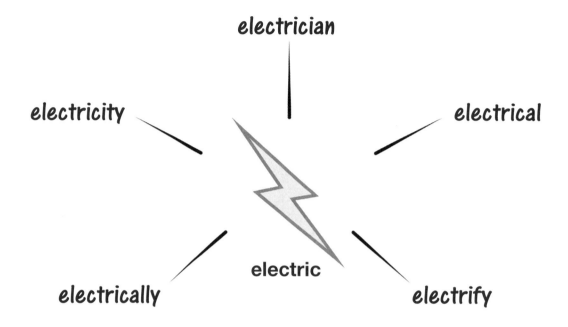

Word families (2)

1. Make word families for these words: *technical* and *sign*.

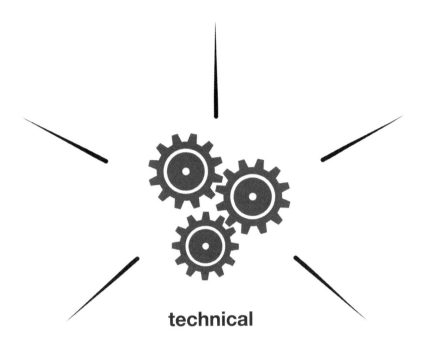

technical

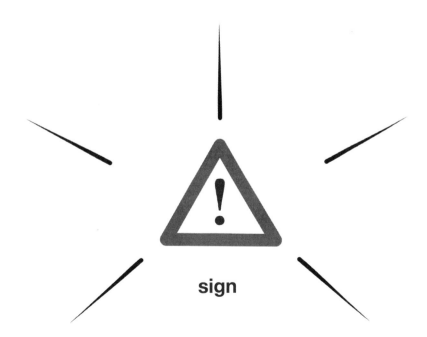

sign

Word families (3)

1. Make word families for these words: *graph* and *science*.

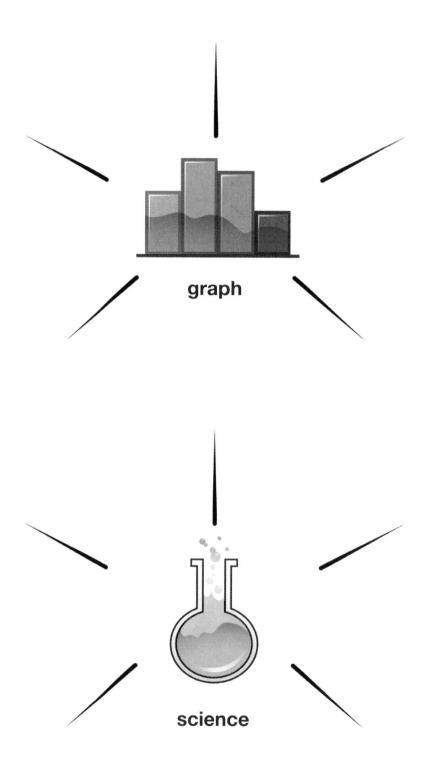

graph

science

Expanded noun phrases

1. Underline the simple noun phrases in the sentences below. Then expand them. The first one has been done for you. If there is more than one noun in the sentence you can choose which one to expand.

a. I ran under <u>the shelter</u> to get out of the rain.

   I ran under the rusty old bus shelter to get out of the rain.

b. There are three apples in the bowl.

   _____

   _____

c. I think it was those boys!

   _____

   _____

d. I wanted to find a red dress for the party

   _____

   _____

e. Four horses raced around the track.

   _____

   _____

Describe these pictures

1. Choose four pictures and write a sentence about each of them.
   Include an expanded noun phrase in each sentence.

good witch

bad witch

talking rabbit

fortress of doom

deep dark forest

murky swamp

treasure chest

magic mirror

book of spells

I done it well

1. Read the speech bubbles and then change the conversation into standard English.

I done it without her.

You was supposed to help each other.

I were thinking this was faster.

But she don't care about that.

_____

_____

_____

_____

Trudy's dream present

Pronouns are used to avoid repetition across sentences.

Read Version 1 of *Trudy's Dream Present*, an example of a writer not using any personal pronouns.

Now read Version 2 of *Trudy's Dream Present*, an example of a writer using too many personal pronouns.

Version 1

Trudy got Trudy's dream present for Christmas – a mobile phone. Trudy couldn't wait to try the mobile phone out, so Trudy dialled a number. Trudy was disappointed when nothing happened. Then Trudy realised that Trudy hadn't turned the mobile phone on. Trudy flicked the switch and tried again, but again Trudy was disappointed because the mobile phone was still dead. Just then, Trudy's friend, Trisha, came into the room. Trudy told Trisha that Trudy had got a mobile phone for Christmas. 'Great, so has Trisha!' said Trisha. 'Trudy and Trisha can call each other!' Trudy said that Trudy had tried but the mobile phone wouldn't work. Trisha asked if Trisha could have a look. Trisha looked at the battery indicator. 'Trisha thought so,' said Trisha. 'Trudy hasn't charged the battery!'

Version 2

She got her dream present for Christmas – a mobile phone. She couldn't wait to try it out, so she dialled a number. She was disappointed when nothing happened. Then she realised that she hadn't turned it on. She flicked the switch and tried again, but again she was disappointed because the phone was still dead. Just then, her friend came into the room. She told her that she had got a mobile phone for Christmas. 'Great, so have I,' she said. 'We can call each other!' She said that she had tried but it wouldn't work. She asked if she could have a look. She looked at the battery indicator. 'I thought so,' said she. 'You haven't charged the battery!'

1. Write your own version of *Trudy's Dream Present* with the right balance of pronouns and proper nouns.

_____

_____

_____

_____

_____

_____

_____

_____

_____

_____

_____

_____

_____

Singular to plural

There are lots of rules about how to show that nouns are plural.

- For most nouns, add **'s'**.
- Nouns ending in **'s'**, **'ss'**, **'sh'**, **'ch'**, **'x'** and **'z'**, add **'es'**.
- Nouns ending in **'y'**, take off the **'y'** and add **'ies'**.
- Nouns ending in **'f'**, take off the **'f'** and add **'ves'**.

1. **Change these sentences from *singular* to *plural* by changing nouns, verbs, pronouns and other words where necessary. An example has been done for you.**

The boy walks his dog.

The boys walk their dogs.

The ship hit the iceberg.

_____

Her tooth hurts badly.

_____

The horse is eating a raw carrot.

_____

The cat chased the mouse through the house.

_____

She heard the echo in the cave.

_____

Apostrophes

Apostrophes can be used to show that something belongs to someone or something.

- *The dog's basket* – the basket belongs to the dog

1. **Read the sentences below. Circle the words that are missing the possessive apostrophe and write them correctly.**

   a. The strong wind blew Olivias umbrella away. _____

   b. The rain battered the horses stable. _____

   c. I saw the rabbits tail. _____

   d. The man fixed the boats rudder. _____

   e. The dogs ball rolled under the fence. _____

   f. I looked at my friends picture. _____

   g. The cars brakes squealed when it stopped. _____

   h. I like my brothers new bike. _____

The cows' garage

Remember: when you add an apostrophe to a plural noun you just add the apostrophe because there is already an **'s'** at the end.

1. Change the singular nouns into plurals and then match them to an object. Add the apostrophe correctly.

2. Complete the final row in the table with your own idea.

the girl___	school	*the girls' school*
the rabbit___	hutch	
the boy___	changing room	
the bird___	nest	
the car___	garage	
the cow___	field	
the ___	___	

Irregular plurals and apostrophes

There are some plurals that are irregular and do not end in an **'s'**. To make the possessive, add apostrophe and **'s'** to these irregular words: *mice – mice's*

When a singular proper noun ends in **'s'** then you add an apostrophe and another **'s'**: Lewis – Lewis's

1. **Put these irregular nouns through the apostrophe tunnel.**

children

Mrs Jones

sheep

geese

men

people

Paris

Chris

Before you go

1. **Complete the sentences by adding the fronted adverbials. Don't forget to add a comma too.**

Before you go   In the morning light

As soon as I'm back   Playtime over

After midnight   In one week's time

_____ I'll be at the concert. Yay!

_____ Hampton Villa was a regular hotel.

_____ it became truly spooky.

_____ don't forget to lock the door.

_____ the class got back to work.

_____ I'll get your dinner ready.

The three little pigs

1. Add speech marks and commas to the passage to show what the characters said.

Poor Mrs Porker couldn't find anywhere to lie down. She turned round and round, trying to find a space because she really wanted to take a nap.

First she trod straight on one fat pink piglet.

That's it! cried Mrs Porker. You're far too big to be a piglet she told him. You must go and find your own home.

So First Little Pig left and went off to find a new home. Off I go he sang cheerily, to find a pretty new house.

Mrs Porker tried to find space to lie down again. She turned round and round and trod on the second fat pink piglet.

You're too big to be a piglet she told him. You must go and find your own home.

So Second Little Pig set off to find a new home. Off I go he sang to find a warm new house.

Again Mrs Porker turned round and round and trod on the third fat pink piglet.

You're much too big to be a piglet she told him. Go and find your own home.

So Third Little Pig set off to find a new house. Off I go, he sang cheerily, to find a strong new house.

And so all the Little Pigs trotted off down the road to find new homes.

Mrs Porker turned round and round found a comfy spot and was soon snoring happily.

Model dialogue

Look at this example of dialogue and notice the use of punctuation and indentations.

Tim and Tom spent most of the afternoon in the shed trying to make aeroplanes from kits – but everything seemed to go wrong.

"Hey, my aeroplane's got four wings," said Tim.

"Mine hasn't got any," said Tom.

"Mine's got four engines," said Tim.

"Mine must be a glider," said Tom.

Then they realised that they had got the parts of the two kits muddled up and the only thing to do was to pull them to pieces and start again.

1. Use the example to help you write your own short dialogue.

Write a short paragraph to introduce the dialogue.

_____

_____

_____

Now add at least three lines of dialogue.

_____

_____

_____

Write a short paragraph to say what happens next.

_____

_____

Easy tent

1. Read the EASY-TENT instructions.

   a. Circle the following and label them: list of what is needed, sequenced steps.

   b. Find any command verbs and highlight them.

   c. Find any words expressing time and highlight them in a different colour.

How to set up your EASY-TENT

1. Check that you have everything you need:
    - The green outer tent
    - The white inner tent
    - The super pump
    - Fully charged batteries
    - 8 large plastic pegs

2. Connect the super pump to the inlet valve on the green outer tent by removing the red cap, and screwing the plastic hose into position.

3. Switch on the super pump. After about five minutes, the green outer tent should have risen to a dome shape. When this is firm and round, switch off the pump and remove the plastic hose. A one-way valve will stop the air escaping, but remember to replace the red cap just to make sure! Note: if the pump fails or the batteries go flat, you will find an emergency nozzle near the inlet valve. Use this to blow up the tent by mouth.

4. Important: Immediately peg the green tent to the ground by placing pegs through all of the eight loops. The EASY-TENT is very light and may get blown away if you forget to do this!

5. Place the white inner tent inside the green outer tent and pump up in the same way.

6. Your EASY-TENT is now ready. Enjoy your holiday!

Story order

The plot of a story is the sequence of main events. This is what happens to your characters at the beginning, middle and then the end.

Introduction: The characters are introduced, the setting described and the theme established.

Build up: What is happening to the characters – often more about the theme.

Conflict: The actions of solving the problem/mystery.

Climax: When the characters are about to solve the problem/mystery and it looks like it either could be solved or not.

Resolution: The problem/mystery is solved and how the characters are affected by the outcome.

They had not gone far when their jeep was stopped by a tree which had fallen across the trail. As soon as they got out to move it, they found themselves surrounded by bandits with AK47 rifles. Tom groaned, and Lindsey wept – but Paco laughed. He knew these men, and after a few words in Spanish, and the gift of a bottle of whisky, they were on their way again.

Tom had heard the legend of the 'Dinosaurs on Dinosaur Plateau' and decided that he would like to be the first to bring back a real dinosaur egg. So he gave up his job as a Geography teacher and set out with his wife, Lindsey, for Porto Paso.

After a difficult climb, they reached the plateau. There was a movement in bushes ahead, and a creature lifted its head to look at them. The head was huge, scaly and had rows of sharp teeth.
   "A dinosaur!" shouted Tom.
   "No," said Lindsey sadly, "only a monitor lizard."

When they arrived in Porto Paso, they bought a jeep and supplies for a month. Hiring a local guide was more difficult. They seemed afraid of bandits, gorillas and hostile tribes – but most of all, of the dinosaurs that they thought were living on the plateau. At last they found an old man who agreed to be their guide. His name was Paco.

Read the story sections on page 44.

1. Number the story section paragraphs in the correct order. Write 1–4 in the boxes.

2. Write what you think is the main point of each paragraph.

   1. _____

   2. _____

   3. _____

   4. _____

3. The resolution of this story is missing. Write your own ending below.

_____

_____

_____

_____

_____

_____

The Railway Children

Characters are very important to a story. However, not everything about a character is described. The reader must also make **inferences** to understand the characters better.

From Chapter 1 *(in their old home)*

There were three of them. Roberta was the eldest. Of course, Mothers never have favourites, but if their Mother had had a favourite, it might have been Roberta. Next came Peter, who wished to be an Engineer when he grew up; and the youngest was Phyllis, who meant extremely well.

Mother did not spend all her time in paying dull calls to dull ladies, and sitting dully at home waiting for dull ladies to pay calls to her. She was almost always there, ready to play with the children, and read to them, and help them do their home-lessons. Besides this she used to write stories while they were at school, and read them aloud after tea, and she always made up funny pieces of poetry for their birthdays and for other great occasions, such as the christening of the new kittens, or the refurnishing of the doll's house, or the time when they were getting over the mumps.

From Chapter 11 *(inside a railway tunnel)*

The roar of the advancing train was now louder than the noise you hear when your head is under water in the bath and both taps are running, and you are kicking with your heels against the bath's tin sides. But Peter had shouted for all he was worth, and Bobbie heard him. She dragged Phyllis along to the manhole. Phyllis, of course, tumbled over the wires and grazed both her legs. But they dragged her in, and all three stood in the dark, damp, arch recess while the train roared louder and louder. It seemed as if it would deafen them. And, in the distance, they could see its eyes of fire growing bigger and brighter every instant.

"It is a dragon – I always knew it was – it takes its own shape in here, in the dark," shouted Phyllis. But nobody heard her. You see the train was shouting, too, and its voice was bigger than hers.

E Nesbit

1. **Read the two extracts on page 46 and then complete the chart below.**

Character	Facts	Inferences (and supporting text reference)
Roberta	The eldest child Called Bobbie for short Has had the mumps	Close to her mother. ("if Mother had a favourite… might have been Roberta") Quick thinking, responsible and practical. ("She dragged Phyllis along to the manhole.")
Peter		
Phyllis		
Mother		
The family as a whole		

Two eagle poems

The Eagle

He clasps the crag with crooked hands;
Close to the sun in lonely lands,
Ringed with the azure world, he stands.

The wrinkled sea beneath him crawls;
He watches from his mountain walls,
And like a thunderbolt he falls.

Alfred Lord Tennyson (1809–1892)

eagle

eagle
majestic appearance
power of flight,
king of birds

since ancient times symbol
of strength and courage
Sumerians 5000 years ago
Imperial Rome
America

but a killer
a dive bomber
with laser sights
that always hits its target

Malcolm George (1950–)

Read the poems and then answer the questions.

1. What are these poems about? _____

2. Which of the poems rhymes? How does it rhyme?

_____

3. What type of poem is 'eagle'?

rhyming ☐

free verse ☐

haiku ☐

Free verse a poem that doesn't follow any rules about rhyming or how to write it.

Haiku a poem that follows strict rules of using only three lines and only using words which make up five syllables on the first and last lines and seven on the middle line.

4. Why does the poet of 'The Eagle' use the word *thunderbolt* when describing the eagle?

_____

5. Why does the poet in the second poem write it as a list?

_____

6. What does *laser sights* mean in the last verse?

_____

7. Which poem do you prefer, and why?

_____

_____

Skyliner journey

Dear Sir

I have just got back from my holiday in New York by Skyliner and I have several complaints.

My first complaint is that Skyliner was SLOW! It took 11 hours to get from London to New York, though your advertisement promised eight hours. What is the point of a new type of air transport if it is slower than the types we already have?

Another point is that I did not get a private cabin. I had to sit in an aeroplane-type seat (though I admit there was plenty of space for my legs). Also, I was not allowed in the glass-bottomed swimming pool. This was very disappointing, because I had looked forward to 'swimming through the sky' as you promised in your advertisement.

It was good to be able to sit at a table for a meal, although you did not say in your advertisement that the cost of the meal was extra. Furthermore, the prices were shocking! I had to pay £25 for pizza, sausage and beans!

I was also very disappointed that the observation deck was open only for the last hour of the journey – and then it got very crowded. However, I must say how much I enjoyed flying over New York and ending our journey at the mooring pole on top of the Statue of Liberty.

Overall, I think Skyliner has some good points, but you need to sort out the problems I have mentioned, and make your advertising more honest. Also, I hope you will be able to offer some compensation for the disappointments suffered.

Yours faithfully

Joe Bloggs

Read the letter and then answer the questions below.

1. **What is Skyliner?**

   A new type of water transport ☐

   A new type of air transport ☐

   A new type of land transport ☐

2. **List three complaints from the letter.**

   _____

   _____

3. **Find and write any words that provoke emotion and any which have been repeated.**

   _____

4. **Can you find the following sentence types in the passage? Write examples.**

   Statements ☐ _____

   Exclamations ☐ _____

   Questions ☐ _____

5. **What is the writer trying to persuade Skyliner Ltd to do?**

   _____

   _____

Composition

Writing paragraphs

1. **Read the text below and organise the story into sections about a theme. Decide when the story starts, when the time changes and when the place changes. Mark these changes with the symbol //.**

It was the morning of the big game. James snuggled into the warmth of his duvet, thinking nervously about the day ahead of him. At 8 o'clock his alarm rang. He sighed. This meant he had to get up. He flung back the duvet and eased his feet into his slippers. Finally he made his way across the room. In the kitchen his dad was cooking breakfast. James knew his dad was only trying to help, but he felt too sick to eat. Across the street Ezzie was ready. As he put new laces in his boots he thought about winning the match. He was sure his team would win. He couldn't wait.

2. **Write the next two paragraphs in the story.**

_____

_____

_____

_____

_____

_____

_____

_____

_____

_____

_____

Driving guide

Instructions must always follow a clear and correct order.

1. **Number the instructions for 'Setting off' in the correct order.**

Setting off

☐ As the car gains speed, change gear until you are in top gear.

☐ Check that the car is in neutral gear.

☐ Check that the handbrake is on.

☐ If all is clear, release the handbrake, and pull out.

☐ Check in the mirror.

☐ Engage first gear.

☐ Get in the car.

☐ Put your seatbelt on.

☐ Start the engine.

2. **Write instructions for a driver approaching traffic lights. Don't forget instructions have:**
   - a clear sequence of numbered steps
   - command-style verbs at the beginning of each step
   - specific detail (measurements)
   - words expressing time (*next, then*).

_____

_____

_____

_____

Develop the setting

1. Continue the setting description.

The sand felt hot and grainy under his bare feet. The tide was out and a wide stretch of shining brown mud lay between him and the water.

_____

_____

_____

_____

_____

_____

_____

_____

_____

Hints: What else can he feel? What can he hear? What else can he see?

Characters in adventure stories

When you plan a story it is important to plan your ***characters***. The characters are who your story is about. Your characters will also help you plan your setting and your plot.

1. List words which describe the behaviours and personalities of adventure story heroes/heroines and villains.

Heroes and heroines

Ideas
helpful   selfish   unkind   determined   inconsiderate
devious   cowardly   thoughtful   trustworthy   hurts others
helps others   never gives up

Villains

Taking exercise

Explanations often use:

- clear steps to explain how something happens and why
- illustrations/photos/diagrams with labels/captions
- subheadings
- words to express time and cause
- specific detail

1. Exercise is good for our bodies. Find out why and write down three reasons.

    1. _____

    2. _____

    3. _____

2. Choose a sport and write about it here using some of the features given in the bullet list above.

Five-point plan

1. **Choose one of the questions in the box below. Use the planning frame to write the first draft of a piece of writing in which you present your point of view on the topic.**

> Should children wear school uniform?   Should chocolate be banned?
> Should children go to school?

Make a point: state your main point and give reasons to support it.

Add another point: give reasons to support it.

Introduce an opposing point: state the opposition's strongest point and give reasons against it.

Discuss the ideas: compare what would happen with your ideas and those of the opposition.

Sum up: state the conclusion you have come to and why.

Fiction writing frame

1. **Use this planning sheet to help you plan a story.**

Character	Setting
What do they look like? What is their personality like? Do they have a family? Where do they live? What are they doing?	Where do they live? What does it look like – in the mountains, by the beach, in a city?

Plot

Introduction

Build up

Conflict

Climax

Resolution

Remember to use:
- capital letters
- end of sentence punctuation
- speech marks (if you have dialogue)
- conjunctions, prepositions and adverbs.

Tip: Try to group your ideas about what happens to your character as this will help you to write paragraphs.

2. **Now write your story on a separate sheet of paper.**

Non-fiction writing frame

1. How do we travel on the water? What do we travel on? Make a list in the lighthouse on the right.

2. Choose one form of water travel and find out as much as you can about it. When was it invented? How does it move? What is it made from? What else can you find out?

3. Now write about your choice on a separate sheet of paper.

Progress chart

Making progress? Tick (✔) the flower boxes as you complete each section of the book.

Spelling

Vocabulary

Punctuation

Composition

Grammar

Comprehension

Well done!

YOU DID IT! ★

Name: _____

You have completed

YEAR 4 ENGLISH

Practice Book

Age: _____   Date: _____

Answers

The answers are given below. They are referenced by page number and where applicable, question number. The answers usually only include the information the children are expected to give.

Note that answers in literacy will be varied and subjective from child to child, and a fair degree of marker discretion and interpretation is needed, particularly if children's understanding and skills have to be deduced from their answers.

Page number	Question number	Answers
6	1	forget, limit, begin, target, travel, regret, visit, prefer, permit, fuel, admit, focus
	2	forgetting, limiting, beginning, targeting, travelling, regretting, visiting, preferring, permitting, fuelling, admitting, focusing
7	1	pyramid, myth, pterodactyl, oxygen, lyrics, cygnet, crystal, mystery
		m y s t e r y h u c o h y o r d p y r a m i d u t g a l y l a k e n u y t o w l r e o f h c r m o t x o y r e n d u y i r y y o a i g n e s n p c g e d w t h y t h n f b a x s y r e x n l o i l y r i c s i n
8	1	country – A place where people live. encourage – To try to make someone or something do something. hound – Another word for a dog. mousse – A light dessert made from egg and sugar. nourish – To give food for things to grow healthily. flourish – To grow successfully. dough – Baked to make bread. couple – Two things together. young – Having lived for a short time.
	2	hound, mousse, dough Children's own answers.
	3	Children's own answers.
9	1	**Across:** 2. irresistible, 4. impossible, 6. illogical, 7. misplaced **Down:** 1. irregular, 3. invisible, 5. disappeared

Page number	Question number	Answers
10	1a	recover
	1b	interface
	1c	interval
	1d	rearrange
	1e	intergalactic
	1f	redecorate
	1g	international
	1h	retreat
11	1	autograph, antibacterial, antisocial, autobiography, anticlimax, antidandruff, autocorrect, anticlockwise, antibody, antivirus, antifreeze, autopilot
12	2a	admiration
	2b	translation
	2c	accommodation
	2d	relocation
	2e	animation
	2f	anticipation
	2g	education
	2h	identification
	2i	justification
	2j	observation
13	1a	Children's own answers.
	1b	Children's own answers.
	1c	Children's own answers.
	1d	Children's own answers.
	1e	Children's own answers.
	1f	Children's own answers.
	1g	Children's own answers.
	1h	Children's own answers.
	1i	Children's own answers.
	1j	Children's own answers.
	2	quickly, anxiously, Fortunately, rather, so, momentarily, again, cautiously, Suddenly, violently
14	1	dramatically, frantically, historically, domestically, energetically, diplomatically, robotically, tragically
	2	Children's own answers.

Page number	Question number	Answers
15	1a	division
	1b	collision
	1c	diversion
	1d	confusion
	1e	corrosion
	1f	comprehension
	1g	revision
	1h	allusion
16	1	politician, dietician, beautician, musician, optician, physician, electrician, magician, mathematician
17	1	confession / conclusion / discussion / confusion / admission / completion / transmission / obstruction / adoption / explosion

```
s c o n f e s s i o n h t
d o d c b u i o s s e l o
i n n a d o p t i o n o t
s f s e a u g h s b a k r
c u x c a n d u r s d o a
u s y c o m p l e t i o n
s i s t s t e s s r r s s
s o m r e d e d e u s s m
i n a a m r t y u c i p i
o e t e a b r o u t v e s
n s s a d m i s s i o n s
o s e x p l o s i o n r i
c o n c l u s i o n c f o
i b d d s s i o n s u k c n
```

Page number	Question number	Answers
18	1	chandelier, stomach, chalet, scheme, orchestra, architect, moustache, parachute
	2	sh, k, sh, k, k, k, sh, sh
19		

```
p h y s i q u e q
i q u e s c i f u
n u n i q u e a e
t g r u f n b t g
r u d a s u g i u
i e c n s e u g e
g r o t e s q u e
u c i i a s c e t
e n o q g u e l i
q u e u f q u e l
g h b e a d d t h
o p a q u e b h d
c o l l e a g u e
```

Page number	Question number	Answers
20	1	**/s/:** scented, descent, discipline, adolescent, oscillate, ascent **/s/k/:** escape, scream, scooter, score, disco, scarf
	2	**/s/:** e, i **/s/k/:** a, o, r
21	1	Children's own answers.
22	1	bee, sea, knew, blue
23	1	write, here, weather, seen
	2	Children's own answers.
24	1	fair, missed, piece, groan
	2	

```
f a r e s s g h
a c m r e f h m
p o i f a i r i
i g s h o d i s
e r t i p l a s
c o e p e a c e
e w s a d r m d
x n s g r o a n
```

Page number	Question number	Answers
25	1a	buoy
	1b	serials
	1c	queue
	1d	yew
	1e	died
	1f	knead
	1g	hair
	1h	fur
	1i	facts
	1j	mayor
	2	Children's own answers.
26	1	ultraviolet, undercover, ultrasound, transport, underarm, ultramarine, transatlantic, underground, translate
27	1	Children's own answers.
28	1	profession, professor, professional, professed
29	1	**Technical:** technically, technician, technicolour, technique, techno, technology, etc. **Sign:** signal, signature, signalman, significance, signify, etc.
30	1	**Graph:** autograph, grapheme, radiography, calligraphy, graphite, etc. **Science:** scientist, scientific, neuroscience, conscience, etc.

Page number	Question number	Answers
31	1a	the shelter/the rain Children's own answers.
	1b	three apples/the bowl Children's own answers.
	1c	those boys Children's own answers.
	1d	a red dress/the party Children's own answers.
	1e	four horses/the track Children's own answers.
32	1	Children's own answers.
33	1	I did it without her. I thought this was faster. You were supposed to help each other. But she doesn't care about that.
35	1	Children's own answers.
36	1	The ships hit the icebergs. Her teeth hurt badly. The horses are eating raw carrots. The cats chased the mice through the houses. She/They heard the echoes in the caves.
37	1a	Olivia's
	1b	horse's / horses'
	1c	rabbit's
	1d	boat's
	1e	dog's
	1f	friend's
	1g	car's
	1h	brother's
38	1	the girls' school, the rabbits' hutch, the boys' changing room, the birds' nest, the cars' garage, the cows' field
	2	Children's own answers.
39	1	children's, Mrs Jones's, sheep's, geese's, men's, people's, Paris's, Chris's
40	1	In one week's time, I'll be at the concert. Yay! In the morning light, Hampton Villa was a regular hotel. After midnight, it became truly spooky. Before you go, don't forget to lock the door. Playtime over, the class got back to work. As soon as I'm back, I'll get your dinner ready.

Page number	Question number	Answers
41	1	Poor Mrs Porker couldn't find anywhere to lie down. She turned round and round, trying to find a space because she really wanted to take a nap. First she trod straight on one fat pink piglet. "That's it!" cried Mrs Porker. "You're far too big to be a piglet," she told him. "You must go and find your own home." So First Little Pig left and went off to find a new home. "Off I go," he sang cheerily, "to find a pretty new house." Mrs Porker tried to find space to lie down again. She turned round and round and trod on the second fat pink piglet. "You're too big to be a piglet," she told him. "You must go and find your own home." So Second Little Pig set off to find a new home. "Off I go," he sang, "to find a warm new house." Again Mrs Porker turned round and round and trod on the third fat pink piglet. "You're much too big to be a piglet," she told him. "Go and find your own home." So Third Little Pig set off to find a new house. "Off I go," he sang cheerily, "to find a strong new house." And so all the Little Pigs trotted off down the road to find new homes. Mrs Porker turned round and round, found a comfy spot and was soon snoring happily.
42	1	Children's own answers.
43	1a	The following should be circled: The green outer tent The white inner tent The super pump Fully charged batteries 8 large plastic pegs numbered steps 1–6
	1b	The following words should be highlighted: check, connect, switch, remove, remember, replace, find, use, blow, peg, place, enjoy
	1c	The following words should be highlighted in a different colour: after, when, immediately, now
45	1	3, 1, 4, 2
	2	Children's own answers.
	3	Children's own answers.
46	1	Children's own answers.
47	1	Children's own answers.

Page number	Question number	Answers
49	1	Eagles
	2	The first. The end of every line in each verse rhymes.
	3	Free verse
	4	Because the eagle dives quickly and powerfully.
	5	List poems give more emphasis to the few words used.
	6	The eagle's eyes are very good and make it an accurate hunter.
	7	Children's own answers.
51	1	A new type of air transport.
	2	Any three of the following: slow, no private cabin, not allowed in pool, cost of meal extra, price of meal, observation deck only open for an hour and very crowded
	3	Any of the following: complaint(s), promised, What is the point, had to, not allowed, disappointing, had looked forward, shocking, disappointed, crowded, enjoyed, honest, disappointments, suffered
	4	Children's own answers.
	5	Resolve problems experienced. Make advertising more honest. Offer compensation for disappointments suffered.
52	1	Children's own answers showing an understanding of paragraphing.
	2	Children's own answers.
53	1	9. As the car gains speed, change gear until you are in top gear. 7. Check in the mirror. 3. Check that the car is in neutral gear. 6. Engage first gear. 1. Get in the car. 4. Check that the handbrake is on. 2. Put your seatbelt on. 8. If all is clear, release the handbrake, and pull out. 5. Start the engine.
	2	Children's own answers.
54	1	Children's own answers.
55	1	Heroes and heroines: helpful, determined, thoughtful, trustworthy, helps others, never gives up

Villains: selfish, unkind, determined, inconsiderate, devious, cowardly, hurts others, never gives up |
56	1	Children's own answers.
	2	Children's own answers.
57	1	Children's own answers.
58	1	Children's own answers.
	2	Children's own answers.
59	1	Children's own answers.
	2	Children's own answers.
	3	Children's own answers.